Practical SixSigma

Jonathan O'Donnell-Young
and Rudy Pilotto

*serious*consulting

Disclaimer: All care has been taken in the preparation of the information contained herein but no responsibility can be accepted by the publisher or authors for any damages resulting from misinterpretation of this work.

Serious Consulting Pty Ltd
52–54 Rathdowne Street, Carlton, Victoria 3053
www.seriousconsulting.com.au

First published 2006

National Library of Australia Cataloguing-in-Publication Data

O'Donnell-Young, Jonathan, 1964– .
Practical Six Sigma.
1st ed.
Includes index.

ISBN 0 9775430 0 5.

1. Six sigma (Quality control standard). 2. Service industries – Management.
I. Pilotto, Rudy, 1961– . II. Title.

658.4013

Designed and typeset by van de Stadt design
Printed and bound in Australia by Impact Digital 32 Syme St Brunswick

Contents

Foreword

I have been associated with Jonathan and Rudy for approximately ten years. I find that they have the rare ability to combine highly practical and effective approaches to performance improvement that are also based in sound theory. They also possess significant experience in implementation of programs that contribute to bottom-line success across a broad range of industries. I believe their approach to six sigma can add great value by providing organizations with enhanced execution capability at both the strategic and tactical levels.

Dr. Jack Goodwin

BSc, MBA, PhD Production and Operations Management

Visiting Associate Professor Melbourne Business School
University of Melbourne Australia

Visiting Professor Business Administration
University of Witwatersrand, Johannesburg South Africa

Introduction to Practical Six Sigma

What ever you do, wherever you are, you should always be doing something that helps a customer.

As traditional businesses come under increasing competitive challenges you need to look beyond your immediate functions and improve critical processes that impact your customers and your products and services.

Customers are the lifeblood of your business and to ensure that you are doing your utmost to help them you need processes that can help deliver the best possible results.

This is where Six Sigma is of benefit, specifically, Six Sigma helps identify where processes can be improved so they enable you to deliver consistently great products, service and results.

Organisations are deploying Six Sigma so that they can meet and exceed customers' expectations, and achieve their business objectives. Practical Six Sigma, is designed so that you can apply Six Sigma easily and quickly to issues which prevent you from doing your best, and to areas that will give you a competitive advantage.

How to use this book

This book provides you with the information and tools you need to successfully participate in and complete Six Sigma projects.

It is divided into three sections: DMAIC, Toolset, and Resources.

The **introduction** provides a background to and history of Six Sigma, the concepts involved in the methodology, and how it is applied within an organisation.

The DMAIC section is divided into a tollgate model for successful project completion that compliments the Six Sigma DMAIC model's five phases – define, measure, analyse, improve, control (DMAIC).

The **Toolset** section contains the main tools that you will use during a Six Sigma project. Descriptions, examples and templates have been included in this section.

The **Resources** section includes some frequently asked questions about Six Sigma, such as how it applies to you and a **glossary** providing you with further explanation of some of the terms used in the book.

Six Sigma defined

Six Sigma is a quality goal which equates to only 3.4 defects per million opportunities for each product or service transaction.

Sigma (σ) is a Greek letter used in statistics to show variation; the greater the amount of variation, the less likely you are to deliver a consistent service which meets your customer's needs and expectations.

As the variation in a process is reduced, your ability to do accurate work improves; this is because there are fewer things that can go wrong.

This book is easy to use. It utilises Six Sigma improvement methodology and focuses on simple application for fast results.

A brief Six Sigma history

Six Sigma was developed by Motorola during the 1980s. It was part of the company's defence against better quality and better-priced products originating from Japanese manufacturing companies. In the 1970s Motorola sold their Quasar television manufacturing business to a Japanese company. This company manufactured the televisions with 1/20th of the defects and at a cheaper price than Motorola had been able to do, with the same employees and manufacturing equipment. Motorola's executives had to admit that their quality level was poor – and decided to take quality seriously.

Bill Smith, an engineer and statistician working within Motorola began to focus on the process variation methods developed by W. Edwards Deming in order to look for improvements so that the probability of defects occurring was almost zero.

Motorola has documented more than USD$16 Billion in savings as a result of Six Sigma efforts since its introduction in the late 1980s.

From manufacturing to all processes

In the mid 1990s General Electric (GE) adopted Six Sigma and spread it company wide from manufacturing processes to all processes including insurance and finance. Jack Welch's (CEO of GE) mandate was that Six Sigma be applied to every area of the GE business.
To date GE have reported USD$6.6 Billion in annual savings due to their Six Sigma program.

Six Sigma themes

Customer focus

Customer focus is the top priority. Customers are the final judge of whether your services provide value for money. Every customer interaction is an opportunity for them to judge whether you have met their expectations or not.

Therefore, any improvements you make to your processes are focused on benefiting the customer, whether they are internal – within the organisation – or external to it.

Data Focus

Measures are the key to gauging business performance. If you can't measure your performance then how can you improve it? Data and statistical analysis is used to understand the key variables that affect your performance.

DPMO (Defects Per Million Opportunities) is the term that is used to identify the possibility of a defect not meeting customer expectations. Six Sigma equates to 3.4 DPMO.

Understanding variation and its causes is a key component of Six Sigma. The key is to reduce variation so that your processes consistently meet your customer's requirements.

Process Focus

Processes are used to create products and services. As a result, they become the focus of where improvements are made. As you improve your processes, your ability to satisfy your customers also improves.

Six Sigma governance

Accountability

At the project level, the accountability for completing the project and task rests with the Project Team members.

The project's Steering Committee is accountable for removing internal blockers and ensuring cooperation from within the business. The Steering Committee is also accountable for ensuring the Project Team has the resources they need to complete a project successfully. The senior management team is accountable for selecting the areas that will be targeted for improvement.

The senior management team must ensure you are working on the right things, the Six Sigma Project Teams focus on doing those things right!

Six Sigma process

Six Sigma uses a standard methodology to improve processes. It is called DMAIC and stands for: Define, Measure, Analyse, Improve and Control. DMAIC focuses on issues that are critical to customers' perception of your service.

We have tailored the DMAIC process by including 'tollgates' at key stages of the project.

The tollgate model

There are five tollgates. TG1 to TG5.

Tollgate 1 (TG1) – decision to initiate a project. Corresponds to the define phase of the DMAIC model.

Tollgate 2 (TG2) – decision to undertake detailed feasibility. Determines whether the project will be of benefit to the organisation and customers. Corresponds to the beginning of the Measure Phase and Analysis Phase of the DMAIC model.

Tollgate 3 (TG3) – decision to execute the pilot to determine the merits of a potential improvement. Corresponds to the Improve Phase of the DMAIC model.

Tollgate 4 (TG4) – decision to implement solution – standardising the solution across the company. Corresponds to the Control Phase of the DMAIC model.

Tollgate 5 (TG5) – decision to conclude project and publish results. Project wrap up, ensuring that the original purpose of project has been met.

Tollgates are key decision points for Six Sigma project governance. They ensure:

- customers/stakeholders are informed and engaged
- risks are managed
- expenditure is controlled
- management awareness and approval of any delays
- additional focus on project delivery
- problems and issues are identified and addressed as early as possible
- a project is still viable

Each tollgate is based on three factors:

1 Benefits to both the organisation and the customer

2 Project status (requirements, deliverables and progress)

3 Effective use of resources (short and long-term consequences)

Each successful tollgate approves the Six Sigma project only until the next tollgate.

The process for Six Sigma is outlined in the following table:

	Steps	Tools	Output
TG1	Decision to initiate project	Meeting guidelines Tollgate checklist	Minutes TG1 checklist
Define	Set up Steering Committee	Brainstorming Meeting guidelines Team development stages	Minutes Steering Committee list
	Set up Project Team	Brainstorming Meeting guidelines Report guidelines Team development stages	Minutes Project Team list Weekly progress reports#
	Identify customer and business needs	Brainstorming Communication plan guidelines Project specification guidelines SIPOC	Project specification Communication plan
	Formally launch project	Meeting guidelines	Minutes
TG2	Decision to undertake detailed feasibility	Meeting guidelines Tollgate checklist	Minutes TG2 checklist
Measure	Collect and/or collate data	Control charts Pareto analysis	Graphical performance data Detailed process maps
	Map the process	Process flowchart	
Analyse	Identify possible causes of variation	Brainstorming Cause and effect analysis	Graphical performance data
	Determine root causes	Force field analysis Pareto analysis Payoff matrix	
	Propose areas for improvement	Brainstorming Cost benefit analysis Pareto analysis Payoff matrix Report guidelines	Phase report

	Steps	Tools	Output
TG3	Decision to execute pilot	Meeting guidelines Tollgate checklist	Minutes TG3 checklist
Improve	Select pilot areas	Brainstorming Force field analysis Pareto analysis Payoff matrix Rollout plan guidelines Training plan guidelines	Pilot rollout plan Training plan
	Commence pilot	Meeting guidelines Report guidelines	Minutes Pilot progress reports
	Evaluate results of pilot	Brainstorming Cause and effect analysis Cost benefit analysis Pareto analysis Payoff matrix	Graphical performance data
	Develop plan to implement solution	Force field analysis Payoff matrix Report guidelines	Phase report
TG4	Decision to implement solution	Meeting guidelines Tollgate checklist	Minutes TG4 checklist
Control	Develop operational handover plan	Control charts Force field analysis Rollout plan guidelines Training plan guidelines	Operational rollout plan Training plan
	Hand over for implementation	Meeting guidelines	Minutes
	Finalise report	Cost benefit analyses Meeting guidelines Report guidelines	Minutes Final report
TG5	Decision to conclude project	Meeting guidelines Tollgate checklist	Minutes TG5 checklist

#Project leader prepares and distributes weekly progress reports to all Steering Committee members

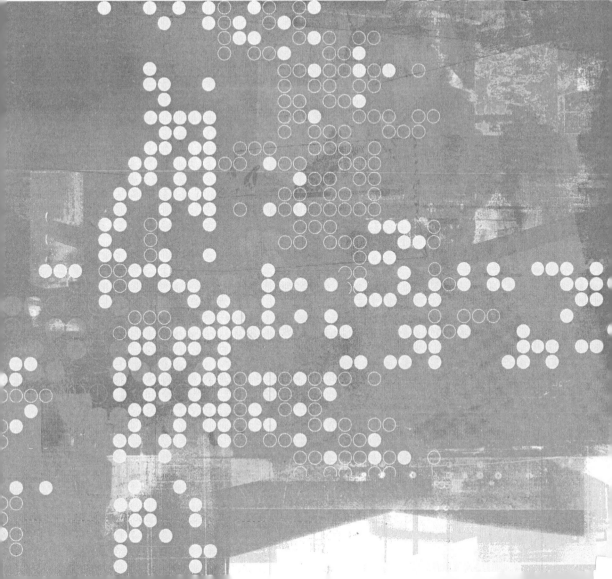

DMAIC

Tollgate One (TG1)

Decision to initiate project

Six Sigma tools	Outputs
• Meeting guidelines • Tollgate checklist	• Minutes • TG1 checklist

Tollgate One has some distinctive features that distinguish it from all subsequent tollgate decisions.

Usually at this stage there is no project steering committee in existence and this tollgate decision is therefore made at a meeting by the:

- person (often the project sponsor) with the need, budget and authority to initiate the project
- a Senior Manager

The purpose of the Define phase decision is to scope and determine the fundamental business viability of the project.

This is the first opportunity to decide whether the organisation will address the proposed issue or problem area and whether it has resources allocated to it.

The project sponsor should complete a detailed Tollgate checklist for TG1.

The Tollgate decision options are:

a Pass the Tollgate and continue according to the agreed plan (with an understanding of the business risk and opportunities).

b Do not start the project (with the reasons documented).

TG1 Decision Options

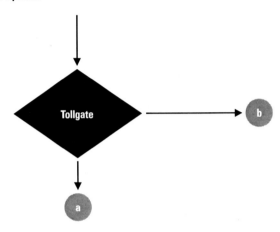

Define

In the Define phase of a Six Sigma project, you spell out the project's purpose in both customer and financial terms and obtain as much background information as possible about the processes concerned.

The Define stage is critical as it allows you to limit the scope of the project to goals that are important to both customers and the organisation. It clearly defines these aims and objectives in a measurable way.

During the Define phase, you select the two groups of people who will be responsible for the project, the Project Team and the governance body (the Steering Committee). Additionally you formally launch the project, notifying and involving all identified stakeholders in the project's success.

The Define stage consists of the following steps:
- set up the Steering Committee
- set up the Project Team
- identify customer and business needs
- formally launch project

The define stage uses the following tools:
- Brainstorming
- Communication plan guidelines

- Meeting guidelines
- Project specification guidelines
- Report guidelines
- SIPOC (Supplier, Inputs, Process, Outputs, Customer process)
- Team development stages
- Tollgate checklist

The define stage produces the following outputs:
- Minutes
- Steering Committee list
- Project Team list
- Project specification
- Communication plan
- Weekly progress reports

Set up the Steering Committee

Six Sigma tools	Outputs
• Brainstorming • Meeting guidelines • Team development stages	• Minutes • Steering Committee list

The Steering Committee is the project's leadership body and made up of key stakeholders in the process.

The desired process improvements of a Six Sigma project are generally experienced across the business, rather than simply within one 'silo' of the business. Therefore, the membership of the Steering Committee of a Six Sigma project represents managers across the impacted areas. Any manager affected by your project should be considered for Steering Committee membership.

The specific roles in a Steering Committee are the chair, project sponsor, project leader and individual Steering Committee members.

A key responsibility of the Steering Committee is to make regular tollgate decisions throughout the life of the project. The purpose of each tollgate decision is that the Steering Committee makes a formal decision regarding whether the project will commence, continue or conclude. The Steering Committee meets monthly, not only for tollgate meetings.

Setting up a Steering Committee consists of the following steps:

1 Assign a Project Sponsor
Identify the person who is willing to 'own' the project and will receive the direct benefits of the project's outcomes. The sponsor can also be, and often is, the process owner. The sponsor has overall 'commercial' responsibility for the project, such as organising funding of the project.

2 Identify and recruit Steering Committee members
Use 'brainstorming' to identify the individuals who can successfully fulfil the eight responsibilities listed below:
- allocating and obtaining required resources
- reviewing the progress of the project
- making tollgate decisions
- helping to quantify the benefits of the project to the other parts of the business
- sharing improvements throughout the organisation
- facilitating the smooth functioning of the project by removing blockers

3 Identify a chairperson
The chairperson facilitates Steering Committee meetings. The chairperson is responsible for ensuring the minutes of all Steering Committee meetings are recorded and circulated.

4 Hold the first Steering Committee meeting
The first Steering Committee meeting is to determine roles and responsibilities, the specific process the team will be improving, and the overall objective of the project.

Set up the Project Team

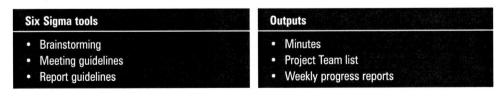

Six Sigma tools	Outputs
• Brainstorming • Meeting guidelines • Report guidelines	• Minutes • Project Team list • Weekly progress reports

The Project Team collects information and provides weekly progress reports to the Steering Committee so they can make informed decisions.

Six Sigma Project Team members possess the necessary aptitude and skills to complete a project successfully. Membership of the Project Team represents all impacted areas of the organisation. Any individual who holds specialist process knowledge and/or hands-on experience should be considered for Project Team membership.

Setting up a Project Team consists of the following steps:

1 Assign a project leader

The project leader is typically a project management trained team member who has the day-to-day responsibility for driving the project. Key responsibilities are to be a member of the Steering Committee and to produce weekly progress reports.

2 Select Project Team members

Use 'brainstorming' to identify appropriate Project Team members based on the competencies and characteristics below:

- **Job/Process knowledge** – good understanding of their role, work and job tasks (inputs, processes, outputs, job requirements, customer criteria and expectations)
- **Cooperation** – willingness and ability to work with others
- **Initiative** – readiness to try new ideas; ability to put forward ideas and suggestions on improvements
- **Customer focus** – an understanding of internal and external customers; a fundamental understanding that all work must satisfy some customer's needs and expectations
- **Interpersonal skills** – the ability to listen and consider different points of view; can present information in a compelling fashion; the ability to establish relationships with other team members and stakeholders

3 Hold the first Project Team meeting

This will be the first meeting where the Project Team get together and:

- allocate roles and responsibilities
- schedule customer and business needs session
- identify people to take part in this brainstorming
- brief the team on the project

Identify customer and business needs

Six Sigma tools	Outputs
• Brainstorming • Communication plan guidelines • Project specification guidelines • SIPOC	• Brainstorming • Project Team list • Communication plan

Identifying customer and business needs defines the issues that the project will address. That is, what is the difference between future customer and business needs and expectations and the current level of service they are receiving?

Identifying customer and business needs consists of the following steps:

1 Perform a SIPOC analysis

The key Six Sigma tool used to identify customer and business needs is SIPOC. SIPOC stands for Suppliers, Inputs, Process, Outputs, Customers and is one of the first activities undertaken by a Six Sigma Project Team.

SIPOC analysis allows a team to focus on customer needs.

It also assists in:

- simplifying an area's many activities down to its priorities as defined by its customers
- identifying whether the customer is getting what they want from you or your area of the organisation
- understanding what the processes do and why
- developing a framework for improvements

2 Produce a project specification

The project specification is a key output of the Define phase and is the document that contains the goals, deliverables and approach of the Six Sigma project.

The purpose of the project specification is to document in one place all project characteristics and constraints at the start of the project.

The project specification is approved at Tollgate Two (TG2) by the Steering Committee and at subsequent tollgates during the course of the project.

It clearly documents the project's:
- purpose
- goals
- scope
- approach
- timing
- budget
- participants
- stakeholders
- logistics and administration

3   Develop a communication plan

The communication plan describes the project's communication strategy. The purpose of the communication plan is to support the achievement of the project goals by:
- assisting the team to monitor and communicate their progress
- keeping stakeholders informed
- keeping the project visibly on-track

Communication takes time and effort, so try to target the plan to those areas that will be able to help the project the most.

Use 'brainstorming' within the Project Team to identify:
- when you will present project information, for example Steering Committee meetings
- what information you will present such as progress reports, benefits, cost savings
- how you will deliver the information, written documentation, stand up presentation, email
- the audience who will receive your communication, for example, stakeholders, team members, senior management, Steering Committee, customers

Formally launch project

Six Sigma tools	Outputs
• Meeting guidelines	• Minutes

The project is formally launched with a meeting that serves as a public statement that the project is beginning. The purpose of the launch meeting is to develop and communicate a shared vision of the project, and to receive a public commitment from all involved in the project's outcome.

Formally launching the project consists of the following steps:

1 Plan and hold a project launch meeting
Project Team members, the Steering Committee and stakeholders attend the meeting.

Topics covered in the launch meeting include:
- description of the project, its outcomes and benefits for customers and the business
- introduction of the Project Team leader and the Project Team members
- identification of the key customers and stakeholders
- the major challenges faced by the project
- what comes next?

Tollgate Two (TG2)

Decision to undertake detailed feasibility

Six Sigma tools	Outputs
• Meeting guidelines • Tollgate checklist	• Minutes • TG2 checklist

The purpose of this tollgate is to determine whether you have completed the Define phase and whether you begin the Measure and Analyse phases.

The Steering Committee will consider the project specification and the communication plan presented by the project leader.

The decision to proceed will be based on:

- business benefits
- project status
- use of resources
- confidence

A detailed Tollgate checklist for TG2 is completed by the Steering Committee at the tollgate decision meeting.

The tollgate decision options are:

a pass the Tollgate and continue according to the agreed plan (with an understanding of the business risk and opportunities)

b do not pass the tollgate (the project must represent further information or a result on a future date)

c stop the project (with all experiences documented)

TG2 Decision Options

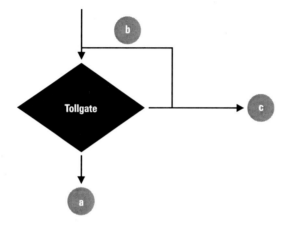

Measure

In the Measure phase of Six Sigma, you gather as much information about the current situation as you can.

You want to be able to show the current performance level versus the customers' requirements. This baseline shows improvements after later phases have occurred.

You also need to map the current process in order to develop an understanding of how the process is actually operating.

You use graphs and statistics because they make the data and processes easier to understand and communicate.

The Measure phase consists of the following steps:

- collect and/or collate data
- map the process

The Measure phase uses the following tools:

- control charts
- Pareto analysis
- process flowcharts

The Measure phase produces the following outputs:

- graphical performance data
- detailed process maps

Collect and/or collate data

Six Sigma tools	Outputs
• Pareto analysis • Control charts	• Graphical performance data

The Measure phase of a project requires that you gather and analyse data that highlights the situation under investigation. You collect and collate data that highlights issues identified in the Define phase.

You also show the current performance level versus the customers' requirements.

Existing data is utilised as much as possible in order to limit the requirement of waiting for new measurements. This will accelerate the Measure phase.

Collecting and collating data consists of the following steps:

1 Identify the types of data you want to collect
It is important to collect data that highlights issues identified in the Define phase. Data can be discrete or continuous. Discrete data is distinct data such as yes/no, on/off, good/bad. Continuous data quantifies the data in a range. Frequency distributions are usually used to evaluate continuous data. For example, the test results for an exam have a range of 0–100 percent. To evaluate the data set, one would use a frequency distribution to understand the data and its variation.

2 Identify sample size for data collection
The correct sample size ensures that you collect just enough data to be able to draw accurate conclusions. Sampling is the process of taking a proportion of the total population for data analysis. Two key elements to consider are that the sampling is representative and random. Representative sampling ensures that the sample accurately reflects the larger population. Random sampling ensures that the sample is not taken with any bias.

3 Determine baseline for measures
Baseline data is basic information gathered before any actual improvements begin.

It is used to provide a comparison for assessing the impact of your solutions. If your project has predetermined goals and objectives these will often provide measures for the baseline data. In most cases, where there is a perceived need to initiate a Six Sigma project, you will already have an indication of what the measures could be for the baseline data. For example:

4 Produce graphical performance data to visually demonstrate the baseline
Present all data and its associated baselines in the following graphical formats:
- Control charts (to show the mean, variation and any trends)
- Pareto charts (to show the major cause components)

Problem	Baseline data
People are spending too much time filling in useless documentation	Measures are: time taken by employees, amount of documentation each employee has to handle, length of documentation, relevance of information.
The process for handling orders takes too long	Measures are: time to process order derived from when order placed to order fulfilled, amount of information required, design of form, regulatory requirements or signoffs.

Map the process

Six Sigma tools	Outputs
• Process flowchart	• Detailed process maps

During this step, you examine the processes involved using process flow charts to identify problems, bottlenecks, areas of waste, error, rework and delays.

It is important to use the knowledge of the Project Team to map what is happening, not just map what documents say should be occurring. The process map captures all steps of the process, identifying all value-adding and non-value- adding activities.

Mapping the process consists of the following steps:

1 Review the current process as documented
It is important that the correct people create the process maps to obtain an accurate reflection of the current process and not only what a few may think it is. The Project Team gathers and reviews all existing process documentation.

2 Review the current process as performed

Does the documented flowchart truly represent the process or procedure? Identify value-adding and non-value-adding activities and all potential and actual problem areas.

Note the decision points in the process; are they in the correct place and do they actually happen?

Look for variation in the way that the documented process is performed. Often this occurs because of organisational or geographical boundaries.

3 Identify all desired process characteristics

Using the results of the above steps and the completed SIPOC from the Define phase, identify the key process characteristics that will achieve both the customers' and the organisation's requirements.

Also identify all auxiliary or supporting processes and/or activities that are key to the process.

4 Identify an optimal process

Finally, develop an optimal version of the process flowchart that will address all of the issues and requirements identified in the preceding three steps.

Versions of a process

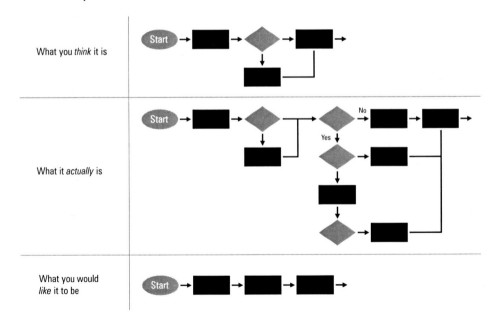

Analyse

In the Analyse phase of Six Sigma, you identify the possible root causes of the problems and then propose solutions to address these root causes.

The Analyse Phase consists of the following steps:

- identify possible causes of variation
- determine root causes
- propose areas for improvement

The Analyse Phase uses the following tools:

- Brainstorming
- Cost benefit analysis
- Cause and effect analysis
- Force field analysis
- Pareto analysis
- Payoff matrix
- Report guidelines

The Analyse Phase produces the following outputs:

- graphical performance data
- phase report

Identify possible causes of variation

Six Sigma tools	Outputs
• Brainstorming • Cause and effect analysis • Pareto analysis • Payoff matrix	• Graphical performance data

Examine the data collected during the Measure phase in order to identify and categorise its variation and the causes of that variation. It is important to do this as it allows you to select the correct strategies for improvement.

Analysing the data consists of the following steps:

1 Identify common and special causes of variation

A convenient way to think about variation is to differentiate between:

- common cause variation – the usual, ever-present variability, and
- special cause variation – the sporadic, 'something unusual has happened' type of variation.

Common cause variation **= stable process**	repeatable many sources common to all occasions and places predictable gives a stable process process is in statistical control
Special cause variation **= unstable process**	onset not predictable increases total variation over and above common cause variation few sources may come and go sporadically gives an unstable process process is out of statistical control

The Project Team 'brainstorm' possible causes of variation and then categorise and prioritise these using Cause and effect, Pareto and Payoff matrix analyses.

Determine root causes

Six Sigma tools	Outputs
• Brainstorming • Cause and effect analysis • Force field analysis • Pareto analysis • Payoff matrix	• Graphical performance data

The possible causes of variation identified in the preceding step are used to determine root causes. Knowing the root causes will allow you to select the most effective possible solutions.

Determining root causes consists of the following steps:

1 Review the possible causes of variation
Examine the outputs of the previous step, paying special attention to differentiate between common and special cause variation.

2 Identify possible root causes
The Project Team 'brainstorms' possible root causes and performs cause and effect analysis, Payoff matrix and force field analyses in order to examine all possible contributing factors.

3 Develop causal hypotheses
Using the output of the preceding step state what you believe to be causing the problem(s) and support this with the data.

4 Produce graphical performance data
Visually demonstrate the causal hypotheses developed in the preceding step.

Propose areas for improvement

Six Sigma tools	Outputs
• Brainstorming • Cost benefit analysis • Pareto analysis • Payoff matrix • Report guidelines	• Phase report

It is obviously not enough to identify only the causes of problems and therefore you now turn your toolset to identifying possible solutions. At this stage, you are interested in using all of the available data to identify the most effective solutions.

Proposing areas for improvement consists of the following steps:

1 Suggest solution to root causes
Potential solutions to the root causes identified in the previous step using brainstorming.

2 Categorise potential solutions
Categorise the results of the brainstorm using Pareto analysis.

3 Analyse the most effective solutions
Cost benefit analysis weighs up the difference between two courses of action; doing something about a particular situation or doing nothing about it.

Cost is a measurement made in economic terms and expressed in dollars. It includes the costs associated with not meeting the customer requirements or non-conformance, known as costs of poor quality; and the sum of the activities undertaken to implement a particular action.

Benefit is also a measure expressed in dollars which measures the economic gain from having implemented the solution and which has removed or reduced the problem/s.

There are many costs associated with poor quality, some that are easy to distinguish (tangible), others that take further investigation (intangible). When undertaking a cost benefit analysis, factor in the 'intangible' costs as well as the tangible costs. For example, intangible costs include lost sales, lost customer loyalty, late delivery. All of these cost your business and represent lost opportunities.

The following table provides examples of the costs of poor quality and the benefits provided by correcting them (ie. the aim of the solutions).

Tangible quality costs	Intangible quality costs
Returns	Damage to brand image
Credits	Loss of morale/employee satisfaction
Reworks and fixes	Employee turnover
Lost production	Lost sales
Overtime	Lost customer loyalty

Tangible savings	Intangible savings
Increase in output	Improved team work
Decrease in waste	Improved customer response time
Decrease in production costs	Increase in innovation/process improvements
Decrease in absenteeism	Increase in brand awareness/satisfaction
Reduction in overtime	Increase in customer satisfaction results
Reduction in turnover	Increase in employee suggestions
Decrease in fault rate	
Increase in size of orders	
Increase of repeat business	
Increase in number of referrals	

4 Determine areas of maximum advantage

Use a Payoff matrix to assess the business payoff each potential solution offers against the associated effort to implement it.

5 Develop phase report

Document all of the results and recommendations in a phase report. Refer to the report guidelines in the toolset.

Tollgate Three (TG3)

Decision to execute pilot

Six Sigma tools	Outputs
• Meeting guidelines • Tollgate checklist	• Minutes • TG3 checklist

The purpose of this third Steering Committee tollgate meeting is to determine whether you have completed the Measure and Analyse phases and whether to begin the Improve phase.

A detailed Tollgate checklist for TG3 is completed by the Steering Committee at the tollgate decision meeting.

The Tollgate decision options are:

a pass the Tollgate and continue according to the agreed plan (with an understanding of the business risk and opportunities)

b do not pass the tollgate (the project must represent further information or a result on a future date)

c stop the project (with all experiences documented)

TG3 Decision Options

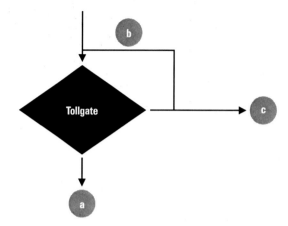

Improve

In the Improve phase of Six Sigma, you develop and test solutions that will address the root causes.

Use data gathered during these trials to evaluate the effectiveness of these solutions and their implementations. The Improve phase is likely to be the longest phase of the DMAIC process.

The Improve phase consists of the following steps:

- select pilot areas
- commence pilot
- evaluate results of pilot
- develop plan to implement solutions

The Improve phase uses the following tools:

- Brainstorming
- Cause and effect analysis
- Cost benefit analysis
- Force field analysis
- Pareto analysis
- Payoff matrix
- Report guidelines

- Training plan guidelines
- Rollout plan guidelines

The Improve phase produces the following outputs:

- pilot rollout plan
- training plan
- graphical performance data
- pilot progress reports
- phase report

Select pilot areas

Six Sigma tools	Outputs
• Brainstorming • Force field analysis • Pareto analysis • Payoff matrix • Rollout plan guidelines • Training plan guidelines	• Graphical performance data • Training plan

Prior to launching improvements on a large scale, you test your solutions. This is known as a pilot. The benefit of a pilot is that it allows you to test and assess your solutions and learn from the implementation.

It is important to note that most improvement initiatives fail because of poor implementation, not the worthiness of the improvement. Any insights gained from the pilot will be invaluable for the wider implementation.

It is best to conduct a pilot in one area of the business, a department, or a geographical area. Results and feedback from the pilot are used to modify and improve the overall implementation.

Selecting pilot areas consists of the following steps:

1 **Identify potential pilot areas**
   Brainstorm potential pilot areas and use Pareto analysis to categorise the results. Use a payoff matrix to identify the most appropriate pilot area.

2 **Plan the pilot rollout**
   Use the rollout plan guidelines to create a pilot rollout plan indicating where and

how you will test your solutions. Force field analyses will help when identifying behavioural and other enabling/restraining forces.

3 Develop training plans

Use the training plan guidelines to develop a comprehensive training plan. Training plans ensure that all staff participating in the pilot understand and are competent in the new processes.

The training plan:

- identifies the target audience for the training
- defines the gap between what current practices are and what they need to be in order to introduce the solution
- identifies performance gaps
  - absence of skill or knowledge
  - absence of incentive or improper incentive
  - absence of environmental and/or system support
  - absence of motivation.

Commence pilot

Six Sigma tools	Outputs
• Meeting guidelines • Report guidelines (pilot progress reports)	• Minutes • Pilot progress reports

During the pilot, the Project Team collects data to determine if the solution is working.

Pilots can often take significant periods and it is important that progress be monitored on a regular basis.

Commencing the pilot consists of the following steps:

1 Plan and hold a pilot launch meeting

All people involved in the pilot attend the meeting, including the Project Team members, the Steering Committee and other key stakeholders.

Topics covered in the pilot launch meeting include:

- a description of the pilot, its outcomes and benefits for customers and the business
- introduction of the Project Team, Steering Committee and key stakeholders
- the major challenges to be faced during the pilot.

2 Perform a mid-execution review

A mid-execution review ensures that the pilot is on track. The Steering Committee reviews the pilot progress reports and considers the following questions:

- Is the pilot on track?
- Have customer needs changed?
- Have any external factors changed?
- Has the project revised its time/cost estimates?
- Has the risk profile changed?
- Is any current or future assistance required?

Evaluate results of pilot

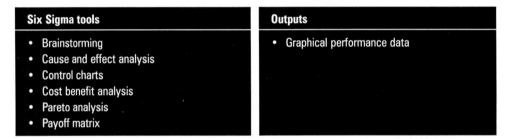

Six Sigma tools	Outputs
• Brainstorming • Cause and effect analysis • Control charts • Cost benefit analysis • Pareto analysis • Payoff matrix	• Graphical performance data

The results of the pilot are analysed to determine whether there has been an improvement compared to the original baseline data.

Evaluating the results of the pilot consists of the following steps:

1 Analysing the data

Evaluate the results of the pilot using control charts, Pareto and cost benefit analyses. Confirm that goals will be achieved if the solution is applied across the business.

2 Identify refinements to the solution

Using participants and other feedback from the pilot, identify possible refinements to the solution and its implementation. Brainstorm refinements and analyse results using Pareto analysis and a payoff matrix.

Develop plan to implement solution

Six Sigma tools	Outputs
• Force field analysis • Payoff matrix • Report guidelines	• Phase report

This plan is an implementation proposal for the Control phase. The plan addresses the areas for improvement and considers costs, timing, resources required and associated risks and opportunities.

Developing a plan to implement solutions consists of the following steps:

1 Prioritise implementation areas
To determine the areas of maximum leverage use a payoff matrix to assess the business payoff each potential implementation area offers against the associated effort to implement it.

2 Consider enablers/blockers
Use force field analyses to consider enabling and restraining forces that could affect the wider deployment of the solution.

3 Produce phase report
Document all of the results and recommendations in a phase report.

Tollgate Four (TG4)

Decision to implement solution

Six Sigma tools	Outputs
• Meeting guidelines • Tollgate checklist	• Minutes • TG4 checklist

The purpose of this tollgate is to review the pilot and decide whether to implement the improvements on a wider scale, embedding them operationally within the organisation.

The Steering Committee considers whether it is appropriate to implement successes from the pilot across all areas.

A detailed Tollgate checklist for TG4 is completed by the Steering Committee at the tollgate decision meeting.

The Tollgate decision options are:

a pass the Tollgate and continue according to the agreed plan (with an understanding of the business risk and opportunities)

b do not pass the tollgate (the project must represent further information or a result on a future date)

c stop the project (with all experiences documented)

TG4 Decision Options

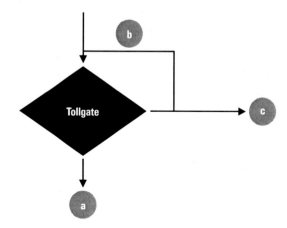

Control

In the Control phase of Six Sigma, you want to maintain the gains you have made by standardising the processes. The Control phase is where the major benefits of the solution are achieved, as it is only when people are competent in the new procedures and use them effectively that all potential benefits will be realised.

The Control phase consists of the following steps:
- develop operational handover plan
- hand over for implementation
- finalise report

The Control phase uses the following tools:
- Control charts
- Cost benefit analysis
- Force field analysis
- Meeting guidelines
- Report guidelines
- Rollout plans guidelines
- Training plan guidelines

The Control phase produces the following outputs:
- operational rollout plan
- training plan

- minutes
- final report

Develop operational handover plan

Six Sigma tools	Outputs
• Control charts • Force field analysis • Rollout plan guidelines • Training plan guidelines	• Operational rollout plan • Training plan

In order to deploy and embed solutions across the organisation, an operational handover plan is developed. This comprehensive plan considers all factors that increase the probability of solutions becoming the new way of working within the organisation.

Developing an operational handover plan consists of the following steps:

1 Create an operational rollout plan
Adapt the pilot rollout plan for wider deployment across the business. Areas for consideration when developing this plan can be found in the rollout plan guidelines.

2 Develop a training program
Use the training plan guidelines to develop a comprehensive training plan that will specify how people will be developed.

Hand over for implementation

Six Sigma tools	Outputs
• Meeting guidelines	• Minutes

The handover for implementation occurs when line managers and those who follow the process – the process owners – take responsibility for the ongoing monitoring and improvement of the process.

Handover for implementation consists of the following activities:

1 Identify process owners
These individuals will take over the ongoing responsibility for managing and

following the new processes. Process owners include senior management, stakeholders and customers.

2 Revise process documentation

Document any variations where business needs or resourcing require an area to adapt the process.

3 Identify areas for improvement

Record all potential improvements. It is important that ownership of further improvement work is clearly identified.

4 Perform handover

Handover of the improved process is done formally at a meeting of all stakeholders.

Finalise report

Six Sigma tools	Outputs
• Meeting guidelines • Cost benefit analysis • Report guidelines (final report)	• Minutes • Final report

The final report represents a summary of the results (against objectives), experiences and observations made during the project. It also includes proposals for improvement of future projects.

The report includes the results of a final cost benefit analysis showing the return on investment to the organisation for having undertaken the project.

Finalising the report consists of the following activities:

1 Conduct a project wash-up meeting

All those who have been involved in the project are given the opportunity to suggest proposals for future improvement. This includes the Project Team, the Steering Committee, stakeholders, customers and suppliers.

2 Perform a final cost benefit analysis

The final cost benefit analysis allows us to determine the return on investment and measure the success of the project.

3 Produce the final report

The final report is circulated to all interested parties for comment prior to its formal submission at the Tollgate (TG5) meeting.

Tollgate Five (TG5)

Decision to conclude project

Six Sigma tools	Outputs
• Meeting guidelines • Tollgate checklist	• Minutes • TG5 checklist

This is the final Steering Committee decision point. TG5 occurs after the completion of project activities (including operational handover) and is a final review and check on the realisation of project benefits across the organisation.

All project successes are maintained and standardised across all areas that benefit from the changes. You may also identify other areas of the business that could benefit.

TG5 is the key opportunity to decide whether to conclude a project. It answers the following questions:

- Are customers satisfied?
- Is the organisation satisfied?
- Were the desired benefits realised/quantified?
- Has organisational learning occurred?
- Are there any future implications/opportunities?

- Is the final report satisfactory?

A detailed Tollgate checklist for TG5 is to be completed by the Steering Committee at the tollgate decision meeting.

The Tollgate decision options are:

a do not pass the tollgate (the project must represent further information or a result on a future date)

b conclude the project with all experiences documented and transferred to the organisation

TG5 Decision Options

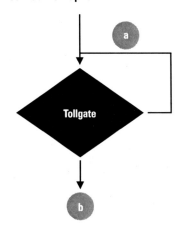

Toolset

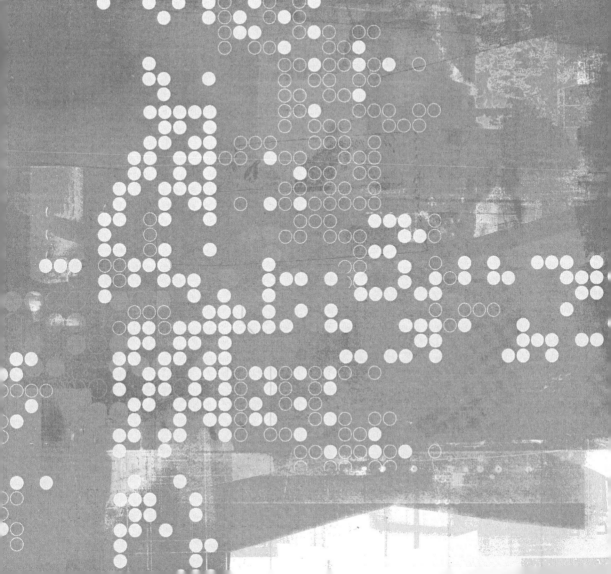

Brainstorming

What

Brainstorming is a process that harnesses the collective thinking power of a group of people to generate ideas.

Why

Brainstorming for quality improvements can be used to:

- identify problems
- analyse causes of problems
- highlight possible solutions

How

Start with one topic at a time. The topic can be a problem to solve, or a new idea.

Write down the topic on a large sheet of paper or on a whiteboard so that everyone in the team can see it. It is important that the team has a scribe to write down all the ideas. This person could also act as a facilitator. The role of the facilitator is to:

- encourage people to come up with ideas
- ensure that no-one speaks over other people
- ensure that no discussion of the ideas takes place

The objective in a brainstorming session is to generate as many ideas as possible – quantity is what counts. If discussion of ideas occurs the brainstorming session may take a long time to complete and people may become dissuaded from contributing ideas.

Once the team has finished the brainstorming session, the ideas can then be evaluated. It is during the evaluation stage that discussion takes place.

Example of a Brain storm

Topic: How to make the perfect espresso.

1	Clean filters	**9**	Tamping
2	Warm up machine & grip	**10**	Amount of coffee
3	Filter water	**11**	Water temperature
4	Grind courseness	**12**	Clean rim of grip
5	Fresh coffee	**13**	Clean machine
6	Grind settings	**14**	Bench space
7	Extraction time	**15**	Training
8	Pressure		

Once the evaluation of ideas has taken place the team can sort them in categories such as:

- easiness to solve
- greatest frustration
- greatest impact on business

Problem versus solution thinking

When setting about brainstorming it is beneficial to ensure that participants maximise the process by ensuring they are using a 'solution thinking' mindset. The focus of solution thinking is about achieving results and planning for them.

Too often time can be wasted by engaging in 'demoralising' discussions about why things can't be done or why things can't change. If this happens it is a recipe for disaster. Therefore, it is important to ensure participants adopt a positive frame of reference by ensuring they are focused on solutions.

The table below provides a helpful frame for getting people to utilise a solution-thinking mind set.

	Problem thinking		Solution thinking
Rather than talk about	– causes, blame – obstacles, frustrations – similar problems	**Talk about**	– the results you want – how to achieve results
Rather than focus on	– the past	**Focus on**	– the future

Cause and effect analysis

What

A cause and effect (or fishbone) diagram is a graphical tool which identifies and displays all possible causes relating to a problem or issue.

Why

A cause and effect analysis can be used to classify the ideas generated from a brainstorm and makes it easier to see patterns or interrelationships.

Cause and effect

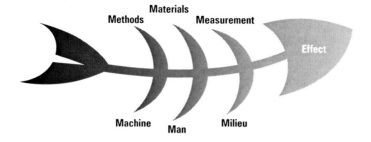

How

When constructing a cause and effect chart the team lists those items that they believe are causes of the problem (effect) under various category headings. The 'rule of thumb' approach is to use the following six headings: Methods, Materials, Measurement, Machine, People and Environment. Of course the team may generate its own category headings.

A cause and effect analysis can be used to classify the ideas generated from a brainstorm. A cause and effect analysis works by grouping similar or related ideas together.

Example of a completed cause and effect diagram

Materials	Method	Machine
Fresh coffee	Tamping	Clean Machine
Filter water	Clean rim of grip	Grind Settings
	Grind courseness	
	Warm up machine & grip	

How to make the perfect espresso

Training	Water temperature	
	Pressure	
	Extraction time	
	Amount of coffee	Bench space
Man	Measurement	Milieu

Toolset

Communication plan guidelines

What

The communication plan describes when, what, how and who your project communication is targeted to.

Why

To develop an effective and efficient communications plan that informs but does not overload the recipients.

How

1 Identify what you want your communication to achieve (for example, awareness, financial support, resources etc.).

2 Identify the individuals and areas (the stakeholders) that you will need to communicate with to achieve the objectives.

3 Identify the key communication messages that will achieve the objectives.

4 Meet with key stakeholders and discuss their communication requirements and preferences with them (NB. For customers this can be done as part of the SIPOC Customer needs analysis).

5 Decide on an appropriate communication format, frequency and channel for each stakeholder.

6 Document as a plan with responsibilities assigned to project team and steering committee members

Communication plan template/example

Objectives	Areas	Key messages	Specific requirements/preferences	Format	Frequency	Channel	Responsible project team member
Active customer involvement and support	Customers Finance	Benefits to customer lead times	Detailed implementation plans	Face to face updates	Weekly	Meeting	Project Leader/ Customer Account Manager
Maintain funding	Project Sponsor	Revenue impact	Short high level overview	Weekly report	Weekly	Meeting	Project leader
Obtain resources	Line managers	Profitability impact	Detailed financial analysis	Tailored report	Monthly	Email	Steering commitee

Control charts

What

Control charts show statistically determined control limits. The control limits show us what the process is capable of doing. They are calculated from the data using easy statistical formulae.

Why

The purpose of the control limits is to provide guidance for action. The limits help separate common cause and special cause variation. The appropriate actions are quite different for common and special causes.

If any of the data points are outside the control limits, a special cause is likely to have occurred. Seek to identify the special cause and prevent it happening again.

If there are no special causes, improvement of the process can only happen if you focus on common causes.

How

To determine if the process is running well or to your specifications, you need to convert a run chart – which shows time ordered data (providing a picture of how the process has been performing) into a control chart. You do this by calculating upper and lower control limits which are +/- 3 standard deviations above and below the mean and account for 99.73% of all variation. Refer to the Frequently Asked

Questions section for the formula for calculating standard deviation. Software for calculating standard deviation and other statistical quantities is readlily available.

Run chart

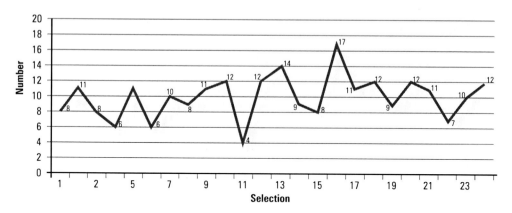

Control chart

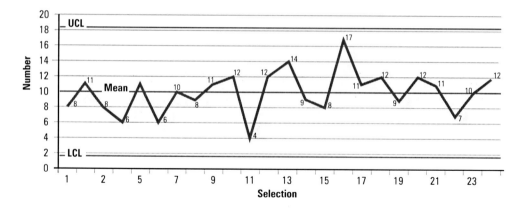

Data from the control chart above represented in a frequency distribution

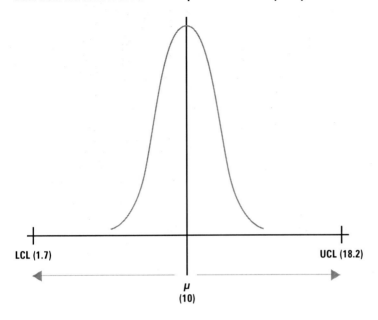

LCL (1.7) UCL (18.2)

μ
(10)

Lower Control (LCL) and Upper Control (UCL) represent the capability limits of the process.

The process mean μ is 10, the LCL is 1.7 and UCL is 18.2. Translated, this means that the probability of a value falling below 1.7 or greater than 18.2 is less than 3 chances in 1000.

Cost benefit analysis

What

A cost benefit analysis is a tool for deciding whether to make a change to an existing situation or process.

It adds up the value of the benefits of a course of action, and then subtracts the costs associated with it to derive an overall analysis of benefit payback.

Why

Solutions to problems may not always be worth implementing, as the investment in time and money in solving the problem may not be worth the effort.

A cost benefit analysis incorporates the effect of time into the analysis by calculating a payback period. This represents the time taken for the benefits of a change to repay its costs.

How

Cost benefit analysis is carried out using financial costs and financial benefits. Enlist the assistance of your accounts/finance department.

Force field analysis

What

A force field analysis is a way of identifying the elements that can help or block your Six Sigma project.

Why

Listing these forces makes clear difficulties as well as the factors that can facilitate the planned changes. The process provides a visual reference which permits you to identify and judge the strengths of the elements at work in the situation.

How

To conduct a force field analysis, begin by stating the outcomes or goals on which you will work. Then list the supporting and restraining forces. Are they within you, your unit, or the organisation as a whole?

After completing your list examine what it tells you. Do the restraining forces outweigh the supporting forces? If so is your objective realistic? Do the supporting forces seem to be stronger? If so, the objective is probably attainable. If the pro and con factors are about even, you can tip the scale in your favour. Simply find ways to reduce the restraining forces.

Making the perfect espresso

+ Driving forces	+ Restraining forces
Love good coffee ⟶	⟵ Too busy to learn
Hit in the morning ⟶	⟵ Machine costs a lot of money
Love idea of brewing my own ⟶	⟵ Sounds very complicated
Want to impress my friends/partner ⟶	⟵ I am the only one who is interested
Consider myself a connoisseur ⟶	⟵ Nowhere to put the machine
Love the smell of freshly brewed coffee ⟶	⟵ Need to remodel kitchen
	⟵ Don't know where to get good supplies

Meeting guidelines

What

A simple procedure which ensures your meetings will stay on track, finish on time and be rewarding for all those in attendance.

Why

No one likes wasting time in meetings so one way to avoid this is to plan your meetings.

How

Use this framework for every project meeting.

1 Purpose and objectives

- Why we are here and what is at stake for us
- Overall progress
- Review previous week's actions and what has happened to date

2 Team review and status of their objectives

- Team members report progress on their objectives
- Teams report on their requirements, obstacles that need to be handled and successes to date

3 Positive reinforcement opportunities

- Recognise what is going well (results and behaviours)
- Recognise what individuals are doing to enable improved performance

4 Team work discussion and action plans

- Develop action plans to meet objectives
- Establish timelines, measures, feedback and consequences for performance against objectives

5 Shared learnings

- Any learning's that are valuable for the team or individuals should be discussed so others can benefit

6 Next meeting

- Key items for discussion next meeting
- Reminder of the next scheduled meeting date

Pareto analysis

What

Pareto analysis, also known as the 80/20 rule (80% of the problems are the result of 20% of the causes), is a tool which uses data to help a team target which factors (causes of a problem) to work on first.

Why

By working on the factor identified as being most important the team's efforts are maximised.

How

Data is used to determine the impact of factors you have identified. Specialised statistical analysis software is also readily available.

If you have no quantifiable data to work with the team can resort to using Pareto Voting.

How to do Pareto voting:

Count the number ideas you have generated from your brainstorm. Divide by the number of people in the group, round up to the next whole integer. The number will equal the number of votes team members have. Then each team member takes it in turns to allocate his/her votes. Count the votes and record the results in the form of a histogram.

Use Pareto voting when:

- you have identified the most important causes of a problem
- you want to determine which area to work on first
- you can't quantify the impact of the causes

Pareto analysis

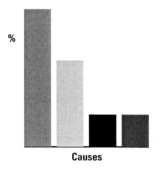

Example of a completed Pareto analysis

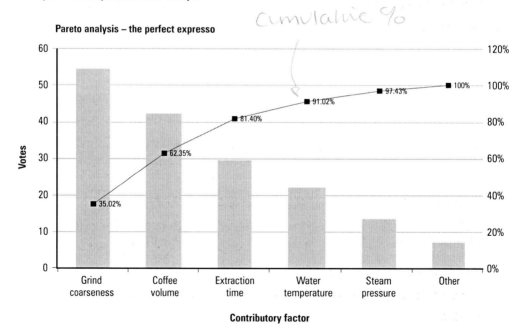

Payoff matrix

What

The payoff matrix is a tool used to prioritise potential solutions.

Why

The payoff matrix helps assess the business payoff a potential solution may offer against the effort to implement it.

How

From the matrix you can gauge how one should tackle any potential solution. The terminology provides us with a good starting point.

- Anything with a low payoff and is hard to do should not be undertaken. DROP these from your planning.

- Activities with a low payoff but that are easy to implement can often provide quick returns and should probably be undertaken anyway. These are known as LOW HANGING FRUIT, easy to pick off but sometimes trivial and with a low return.

- Potential solutions that have high payoffs but are hard to implement. They usually require more diligent effort where perseverance is a must. Known as the HIGH HARDS.

- The JEWELS are the potential solutions that offer high payoffs for less effort than the HIGH HARDS. Aptly named these are the ones you go for.

- In the event that everything ends up in one quadrant apply a payoff matrix to that quadrant.

Prioritisation: the Payoff matrix

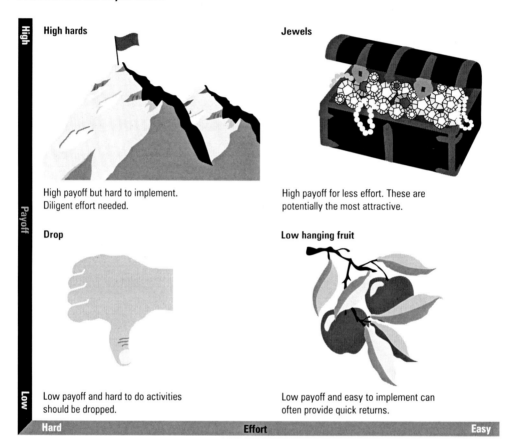

High hards

High payoff but hard to implement. Diligent effort needed.

Jewels

High payoff for less effort. These are potentially the most attractive.

Drop

Low payoff and hard to do activities should be dropped.

Low hanging fruit

Low payoff and easy to implement can often provide quick returns.

Example of a completed payoff matrix

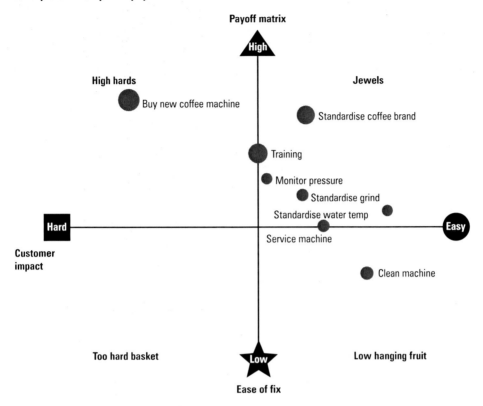

Toolset

Process flowcharting

What

A process flowchart captures the key steps of the process, identifying all value-adding and non-value-adding activities.

Why

Flowcharting allows a team to identify the sequence of activities in a process and highlights bottlenecks, loops and other points of waste, error and rework.

How

Flowcharts use symbols and words to describe the process activities. The standard or basic symbols used in most flowcharts are shown here.

At the beginning and end of an activity, the start and stop symbols are represented by a large ellipse/circle.

Activities are represented by a rectangular box. The flow from one activity to the next is shown using flow lines which indicate the direction of the activities.

A diamond is used if there is a decision or option point during the process flow.

Connector symbols (as circles) are used to connect the activities across pages.

Specialised process mapping software is available commercially.

Basic Flow Chart Symbols

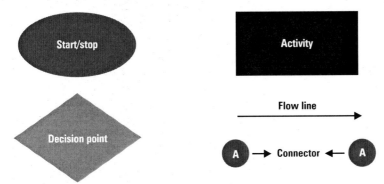

Toolset

Project specification

What

The project specification is a document that details the goals, deliverables and approach of the Six Sigma project.

Why

The project specification sets the ambitions, boundaries and goals for the team.

How

The project team is responsible for developing the project specification. It must be approved by the Project Sponsor and Steering Committee at the TG2 meeting and then communicated to all key stakeholders as identified in the communications plan.

Project specification for: <PROJECT NAME>

Abstract

<A short description of the contents of the document>

BASIC INFORMATION

PURPOSE

Describe the purpose of the project. The purpose should be expressed as a description of the general aim and direction of a project and the expected project result.

BACKGROUND

Put the project into a context by describing the current situation. Describe briefly the reasons and conditions for undertaking this project.

GOALS

PROJECT GOALS

Formulate the project goals. A project goal includes a time limit (ready date), estimated costs and other characteristics.

PROJECT OBJECTIVES

Formulate the project objectives. An objective is subordinate to a goal. Objectives are used to clarify and subdivide project goals. Objectives must be formulated in measurable terms.

MILESTONES/INTERMEDIATE OBJECTIVES

Set any milestones. The milestones must be clear and indicate results as well as time and cost objectives.

EXCLUDED

In order to lock in the project scope and avoid any future shifts in the level of ambition, state what is specifically excluded from the project in relation to its goals.

CONNECTIONS TO OTHER PROJECTS

Specify the links between the project and other projects or assignments.

PLANS

RESOURCE PLAN AND RESOURCE PROFILE

Prepare a resource plan, specifying the project's requirements for human as well as other resources. Prepare resource profiles if appropriate.

PROJECT BUDGET

Prepare budgets for resources and costs.

PROJECT ORGANISATION

ORGANISATION CHART +S\ P0C & applicable

Enclose an organisational chart or present one here.

EXTERNAL CONTACTS

Specify external contacts such as partners, consultants and subcontractors by name and function in the project.

ROLES, RESPONSIBILITY AND AUTHORITY

Specify the participants in the project organization in terms of roles, responsibility and authority.

RISK AND OPPORTUNITIES

Indicate risks and opportunities. Propose ways of avoiding risks and taking advantage of the opportunities.

INTELLECTUAL PROPERTY RIGHTS

State the legal aspects of the project´s results such as patents, copyrights etc.

PROJECT CONCLUSION

Specify how the outcome of the project will be taken care of when the project is concluded, for instance as regards maintenance, implementation, production, sales, operation.

Report guidelines

What

Report guidelines are a set of report templates tailored to the needs of a Six Sigma project.

Why

Six Sigma projects require a number of targeted reports in order to manage the project's progress, to achieve its goals and to share all learnings throughout the organisation.

How

Reports are produced on a regular basis and at specified points during the DMAIC process as below:

- weekly progress reports
- Measure and Analyse phase reports
- Improve phase report
- final report

A specific template is provided for each report.

Weekly progress reports

The project leader is responsible for providing a short weekly progress and issues report to the:

- Steering Committee
- key stakeholders as identified in the communications plan

Weekly progress report template

Progress report for: <PROJECT NAME>

RESULTS ACHIEVED SINCE THE LAST REPORT

Describe briefly the results achieved since the **last report**

Indicate other events of interest that have occurred since the preceding report

EXPECTED RESULT

Describe briefly the result, important events and deliveries expected for the next reporting period

TIME SCHEDULE AND BUDGET

Comment on major deviations from baseline plans with regard to both the current situation and the forecast. Indicate actions that will be taken to make up for delays. If needed, suggest new completion date as well as new costs and resource limits.

Update the project time plan and costing documents as required.

RISKS

Describe any new risks identified or any changes to the status of risks as identified in the project scope document.

ACTIONS

ACTIONS TO BE TAKEN WITHIN PROJECT

Specify actions to be taken within the project.

ACTIONS TO BE TAKEN BY PROJECT SPONSOR OR STEERING GROUP

Specify the actions to be taken or decisions to be made by the Project Sponsor or by the project steering group, to deal with problems stated under the different headings in the Progress Report.

Measure and Analyse phase report

The Measure and Analyse phase report should be produced at the completion of the Measure and Analyse phase and presented for consideration by the Steering Committee at the Tollgate Three decision meeting. It should contain:

Measure and Analyse phase report template

MEASURE AND ANALYSE PHASE OUTPUTS

- Graphical performance data
- Detailed process maps
- Root causes of variation
    - Cause and effect analysis
    - Pareto analysis
    - Payoff matrix
    - ABC analysis
    - Force field analysis
    - Cost benefit analysis

PROPOSAL FOR THE IMPROVE PHASE

- Areas for improvement
- Costs
- Timing
- Resources
- Risks and opportunities

Improve phase report

The Improve phase report should be produced during the Improve phase and presented for consideration by the Steering Committee at the Tollgate Four decision meeting.

Improve phase report template

IMPROVE PHASE OUTPUTS

- Pilot rollout plan

- Training plan

- Pilot progress reports

- Results of mid-execution review

- Evaluated pilot results

    - Cause and effect analysis

    - Pareto analysis

    - Payoff matrix

    - Force field analysis

    - Cost benefit analysis

PROPOSAL FOR THE CONTROL PHASE

- Areas for improvement

- Costs

- Timing

- Resources

- Risks and opportunities

Final report

The final report ensures that each Six Sigma project has achieved all it can and that the organisation learns as much as possible from experiences gained and observations made during the project.

The final report is developed during the Control phase and circulated for comment to all relevant project participants, the Steering Committee and key stakeholders. It is presented at the Tollgate Five meeting for final sign-off and a decision on project conclusion. Subsequently it should be widely communicated and made available within the organisation.

PROJECT SUMMARY
- Purpose
- Results
    - Customer outcomes
    - Business outcomes
    - Final cost benefit analysis
- History
    - DMAIC overview and timeline

EXPERIENCES AND OBSERVATIONS

PROPOSALS FOR FUTURE IMPROVEMENT

Final cost benefit analysis

The final cost benefit analysis should show the total implementation costs, quality costs and the benefits. Also include 'intangible' costs and benefits if possible. These include customer satisfaction, repeat business from customers or referrals, employee satisfaction, employee engagement, discretionary effort.

Rollout plan guidelines

What

A comprehensive set of guidelines which consider all the factors that increase the probability of solutions becoming the new way of working across the organisation.

Why

In order to deploy and embed solutions across the organisation, an effective operational rollout is required.

How

Rollout plans are developed in both the Improve and Control phases of a project. During the Improve phase they are used to plan the pilot, and in the Control phase they are used for the wider deployment of improvements throughout the organisation.

Rollout plan guidelines

PROCESS

- Methods

- Documentation

- Objectives

RESOURCE REQUIREMENTS AND IMPLICATIONS

- People

- Materials

- Communication of changes

- Training requirements (Refer to training plan guidelines)

MEASURES AND DATA COLLECTION

- Baselines

- Ongoing

ORGANISATIONAL REQUIREMENTS AND IMPLICATIONS

SYSTEMS REQUIREMENTS AND IMPLICATIONS

MANAGEMENT AND REPORTING SYSTEMS

SIPOC

What

SIPOC stands for Suppliers, Inputs, Processes, Outputs, Customers – it is the key Six Sigma tool used to identify customer and business needs.

Why

SIPOC encourages a team to focus on customer needs. It also assists in:

- simplifying an area's many activities down to its priorities as defined by its customers
- identifying if the customer is getting what they want from you or your area of the organisation
- understanding the processes involved

How

The starting point with SIPOC analysis is to:

1 Identify your customers

A customer can be defined as anyone who receives the results, or end products, of your work.

Customers can be **internal**; the recipient of another person's or department's output within an organisation, or **external**; a person or organisation who receives a product, a service or information, but is not part of the organisation supplying it.

Use brainstorming to help identify your customers.

It is necessary to prioritise your list of customers so you focus on those who are most vital to your team. Pareto analysis may prove useful in sorting your list.

2 Customer needs

Once you have identified who your customers are, it is necessary to determine what their specific needs are. You can do this simply by asking them, using the customer needs template overleaf.

3 Outputs

Determine your outputs – the products, services or information – you produce to meet your customers' needs.

4 Process

In broad terms, describe the process or processes that are used to create the outputs. Describe what you do and how you and your team works to produce products, services and information.

5 Inputs

In order for you or your team to operate effectively, you require resources either in the form of information, products or services. These resources are known as Supplier Inputs. Ask yourself 'What resources do I need to do my job?'

6 Suppliers

Suppliers provide the resources you need to do your job. For example, marketing may supply you with information regarding customer needs, or your manager may supply you with the direction you require. List your suppliers. Ensure that your list of suppliers is related to your list of supplier inputs.

Once you have completed your SIPOC analysis you should identify, with your customers, areas of improvement. A good starting point is to determine which aspects of the outputs could be improved to better meet customers' needs.

Working with your suppliers, communicate your needs and agree on performance measures and checks.

Example of a completed SIPOC

SIPOC name: Coffee shop

NB Process capability is a function of resources, their competence, the processes in use and the supporting systems in place

Suppliers (Those who provide/ supply the resources you need to do your job.)	Supplier input (Resources received from the suppliers.)	Process (How work is produced)	Output (What you produce)	Customers (Recipients of the outputs)
Coffee supplier	Beans	Coffee making – grinding, extraction, milk	Coffee, café latte, cappuccino	General Public
Dairy Company	Milk	Milk frothing	Chat/gossip	
Confectionary Company	Chocolate	Sprinkling	Change	
Customer	Order	Order taking		
Equipment	Money	Cleaning and Maintenance		
Manufacturer	Espresso Machine Parts			

SIPOC

Suppliers (Those who provide/ supply the resources you need to do your job.)	Supplier inputs (Resources received from the suppliers.)	Processes (How work is produced)	Outputs (What you produce)	Customers (Recipients of the outputs)

Customer name:

List customer needs	Identify your outputs	Determine what aspects of your outputs the customer finds satisfying	Determine which aspects of your outputs could be improved	Identify/create performance measures
Customer needs				

Team development stages

What

Team development stages is a model (also known as Tuckman's team development model) which maps the common development stages of teams.

Why

When setting up your project team you should also be aware of the effects of any team dynamics issues. The objective of any team is to perform, though sometimes teams get stuck and need some assistance to progress.

How

Discuss the team development model with all team members when forming both the project team and the steering committee. Give special focus to the norming phase and don't forget to celebrate and recognise achievements.

Forming

The forming stage of team development is the initial stage where people are brought together to act as a team. Often this stage is characterised by people being cautious and watchful. People will rarely express themselves openly without others leading the way.

Storming

The storming stage is characterised by unproductive conflict and can arise due to an inability of team members to work through issues constructively. This is where team members need to utilise the solution-thinking model to help them. If the team cannot resolve issues they can get stuck at this stage and the team will not become productive. In order to become productive the team needs to move into the next phase ... the norming phase.

Norming

In the norming phase the team establishes a common purpose – answers the questions why are we doing this and what is at stake for us – discusses and achieves clarity and agreement on project outcomes and the method for working as a team.

Finally it clearly establishes roles and responsibilities. Working through the norming phase will avoid the potential for storming.

Performing

The performing stage is characterised by making progress. Your plans are in place and you should be tracking your team's performance. Use the meeting procedure to run meetings and carefully monitor progress. Issues can be worked out constructively using brainstorming and solution thinking.

Celebrating

Once you have completed the project you should take time to acknowledge each other and celebrate the completion and achievement of your goals. Just as it is natural for any sporting team to celebrate success, so too should your team celebrate the successful completion of your project.

Team development stages

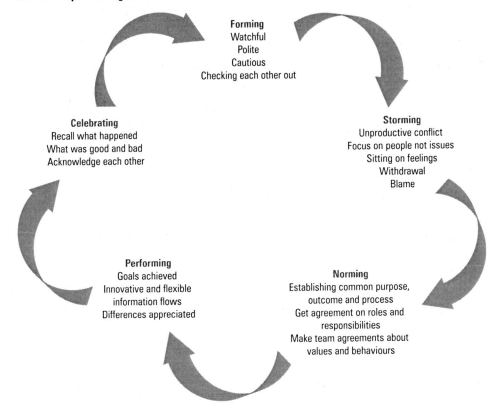

Forming
Watchful
Polite
Cautious
Checking each other out

Storming
Unproductive conflict
Focus on people not issues
Sitting on feelings
Withdrawal
Blame

Celebrating
Recall what happened
What was good and bad
Acknowledge each other

Norming
Establishing common purpose,
outcome and process
Get agreement on roles and
responsibilities
Make team agreements about
values and behaviours

Performing
Goals achieved
Innovative and flexible
information flows
Differences appreciated

Toolset

Tollgate checklists

Tollgate one (TG1)

What

Tollgate checklists are a set of questions designed to be asked by the steering committee at each tollgate decision.

Why

It is important for the clarity of purpose of all project participants and stakeholders that a common and consistent approach to all tollgate decisions is used across all Six Sigma projects.

How

Use the appropriate Tollgate checklist at each tollgate:

- Before the meeting, as a preparatory aid
- During the meeting, as a list of discussion points (it is important to note that answering "no" to a number of questions does not automatically mean that the tollgate cannot be passed. The expertise, experience and discretion of the steering committee are required at each tollgate
- After the meeting, as a record of the decision

Inputs

- Idea for a Six Sigma project
- Estimate of resource requirements

Outcomes

- Minuted decision to start a Six Sigma project and to commence the Define phase including confirmed goals, deliverables and approach
- Complete TG1 checklist (refer below)
- An assigned Project Sponsor

Business benefits	Yes/No	Comments
Are there potential customer benefits from the proposed project outcomes?	Y N ☐ ☐	
Are there clear organisational benefits from the proposed project outcomes?	Y N ☐ ☐	
Are all constraints and non-negotiable issues clearly understood?	Y N ☐ ☐	
Project status		
Is the project within the organisation's mandate?	Y N ☐ ☐	
Is there a timing trigger or window?	☐ ☐	
Does it fit in with other projects/activities	Y N ☐ ☐	
Is the time period for the Define phase acceptable?	Y N ☐ ☐	
Use of resources		
Are the relevant areas appropriately represented in the Define phase?	Y N ☐ ☐	
Are the appropriate resources/ competencies available?	Y N ☐ ☐	
Will the Define Phase require investment (in equipment, locations, and competency development)?	Y N ☐ ☐	
Confidence		
What are the risks of doing the project versus inaction?	Y N ☐ ☐	

Tollgates one, two and three (TG2, TG3 and TG4)

Inputs

- Project specifications (TG2)
- Phase report (TG3 and TG4)

Outcomes

- Minuted decision to continue to the Measure and Analyse phases including confirmed goals, deliverables and approach
- Complete TG2 checklist (refer below)

It should consider the following questions:

Business benefits			
Are there potential customer benefits from the proposed outcomes of the previous phase?	Y ☐	N ☐	
Are there clear organisational benefits from the proposed outcomes?	Y ☐	N ☐	
Are all constraints and non-negotiable issues clearly understood?	Y ☐	N ☐	
Project status			
Are the outputs and report adequate?	Y ☐	N ☐	
Is the time period for the next phase acceptable?	Y ☐	N ☐	
Have issues/risks and opportunities been considered?	Y ☐	N ☐	
Use of resources			
Are the relevant areas/resources appropriately represented?	Y ☐	N ☐	
Will any investment be required (in equipment, locations, and competency development)?	Y ☐	N ☐	
Are the appropriate resources/ competencies available?	Y ☐	N ☐	
Confidence			
Will the project meet its objectives in the desired timeframe?	Y ☐	N ☐	

Tollgate five (TG5)

Inputs

- Final report

Outcomes

- Minuted decision to conclude the Six Sigma project
- Archived master project documentation

It should consider the following questions:

Business benefits	Yes/No	Comments
Did the project outcome produce the desired business results?	Y ☐ N ☐	
Project status		
Have issues/risks and opportunities resulting from the project been considered?	Y ☐ N ☐	
Has the project been successfully handed over to operational management?	Y ☐ N ☐	
Will project conclusion generate any further investments (in equipment, locations, and competency development)?	Y ☐ N ☐	
Use of resources		
Have project resources been reassigned?	Y ☐ N ☐	
Learnings		
Is the *final report* adequate?	☐ ☐	
Has competency transfer from the project been fully addressed?	Y ☐ N ☐	
Confidence		
Is there evidence of ongoing performance measurement?	Y ☐ N ☐	
Does the project require additional follow-up or independent review?	Y ☐ N ☐	

Training plan guidelines

What

A training plan is required to ensure the effective transfer of the skill required to successfully implement the new process. It increases the success of effective learning for participants. It also allows you to get a true cost of the entire training – once you have scoped out the resources, material, venue and time required.

Why

The training plan is a structured way of mapping out capability gaps, context of the training in the workplace, projected costs associated with the training, resources and logistics required, training strategy, delivery method, clear outcomes, promotional strategy for training, assessment and evaluation strategy.

How

A training plan can be customised according to the magnitude of the training required. Clear timeframes should be included against each of the actions within the training plan.

Resources

Frequently asked questions

1 How does Six Sigma apply to what I do?

Six Sigma can be applied to any process. Processes exist in every business and in any function. Six Sigma has been applied to processes in:

- law firms
- transportation companies
- energy supply facilities
- financial institutions
- health care providers
- universities
- government agencies
- insurance providers
- sales forces

These entities have one thing in common; they all complete their business through the use of processes.

Six Sigma can be used to improve any process. The key is determining which 'improved' processes would benefit the company most. These processes may include:

- financial transactions
- logistics and scheduling
- sales and order processing
- customer call centres
- design functions
- supplied goods receipt
- inventory management
- customer service
- marketing and advertising
- purchasing

2 What does the term 'Practical' in Practical Six Sigma mean?

We have chosen to use the term 'Practical' to describe our version of Six Sigma.

Six Sigma is not theoretical or complex; it is designed to be a practical and simple set of useable tools and techniques. Six Sigma can be an easy and integral part of the way you work.

Six Sigma tools and techniques aren't just for use in Six Sigma projects. For example, the meeting guidelines are suitable for all meetings.

3 How will projects be selected?

Using input from customers and employees will identify a list of potential projects. These should be discussed and prioritised and key projects selected as Six Sigma projects.

4 How will this help us to improve customer relationships?

Six Sigma projects involve listening to your customers and delivering results fast. Making sure this happens will help you to improve customer relationships.

5 How does variation affect your experience?

You have moved to a new house and want to know whether it is quicker and more reliable to go to work by car or by train. You decide to test which of the alternatives, car or train, is more reliable by travelling to and from work by car for one week, and travelling to and from work by train for one week.

Time is measured 'door-to-door'. From the time you leave the door of your home to go to work to when you walk through the door of your work place – a coffee shop that you need to have open by 8:00am to catch the office workers before they start work.

While you need to have the shop open by 8:00am, you would like to be there by 7:30am so that you can turn on the coffee machines in time for the 8:00am opening.

It takes 20 minutes for the coffee machines to be ready for use.

Train journey

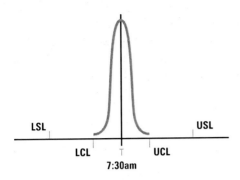

LSL   LCL   T   UCL   USL
7:30am

Car journey

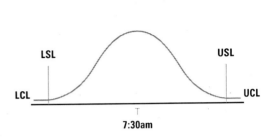

LSL   USL
LCL   UCL
T
7:30am

Raw Data

Car

Day									
M	T	W	T	F	M	T	W	T	F
Journey Time (minutes)									
30	41	58	60	35	46	40	58	42	40

Train

Day									
M	T	W	T	F	M	T	W	T	F
Journey Time (minutes)									
40	41	50	49	42	46	40	49	48	45

To keep the test accurate you standardise the departure times so they are exactly the same for the car and the train. Departure time from home is 6:45am each day.

After 2 weeks you have enough data to help you make a decision as to whether you should go to work by car or train.

On average (mean) both means of transport got you to work at 7:30am. The car managed to get you to work between 7:15am and 7:45am every day. The train managed to get you to work between 7:25am and 7:35am.

Taking the train to work is the best option because it always allows you to open the shop on time and not have customers waiting for their coffee.

This is an example of how variation affects your experience. While the performance average of the car and train was the same it was the variation in performance which affects your perception and your ability to satisfy your customers. If both modes of transport were performing to Six Sigma you would be able to get to work by 7:30am 99.9997% of the time.

6 What does six sigma actually mean?

As an example to illustrate why 99.9997% accuracy is desired over 99% accuracy see the following table:

99% Accuracy (3.8 σ)	99.9997% Accuracy (6 σ)
2523 dropped babies in hospitals every year in Australia	Less than 1 dropped baby
Electricity outages of 3.6 days per year	Electricity outages of less than 2 minutes per year
19.2 hours of computer down time per year	20 seconds of computer downtime per year
47, 800 phone billing errors per month	14 phone billing errors per month

7 Why is 99% not good enough?

When you consider the number of steps involved in a typical work process you quickly come to realise that if every step was performed at 99% accuracy the final recipients of the outputs of the process – the customers – would not be satisfied.

Consider a process which has 5 steps for example, a par 5 on a golf course:

For a 99% level of performance the golfer would receive the result of:

99% x 99% x 99% x 99% x 99% = 95% chance of getting the ball in the cup in 5 shots

For a Six Sigma process (99.9997%) the golfer would receive the result of:

99.9997% x 99.9997% x 99.9997% x 99.9997% x 99.9997% = 99.9985% chance of getting the ball in the cup in 5 shots

Consider a process where teams are performing at different levels and are involved in generating an outcome for a customer:

Team A		Team B		Team C		what the customer gets
100%	x	99%	x	85%	=	84% of what they want

8 What causes variation?

All processes exhibit variation. When we say that two things are the same we often mean that the measurement system we use is not sensitive enough to distinguish between them, or that the difference between them is of no practical importance to us.

Examples of variation:

- time taken to travel to work each day
- amount spent at the supermarket each fortnight
- daily consumption of gas or electricity
- golf scores
- airplane departure and arrival times
- number of errors per 100 documents typed

It is important to understand what the expected range of variability is for any job and to know when something goes outside this range.

Many random fluctuations that are always present and attributable to no single cause and sporadic causes whose identity can often be assigned to a single source. The problem is to decide whether the variability we observe from a process is just part of the usual variability, or whether it shows that something unusual has happened in the process. We want to separate what's just the usual, everyday variability which we expect to see from 'something's gone wrong' – or sometimes to, 'something's gone right'.

9 How do we measure variation?

A measure of spread that identifies the amount of variation is called the standard deviation. It tells us about the spread of a normal distribution. If you think about a bigger and bigger sample of times taken from people's wrist watches, the histogram

that you could draw would get smoother and smoother, and eventually, when you
had a very large number of times, turn into a smooth curve like this:

Standard deviation

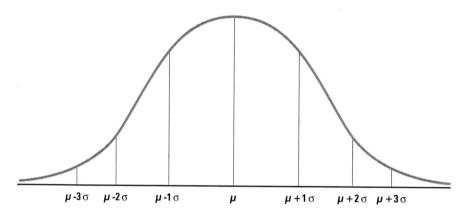

μ-3σ μ-2σ μ-1σ μ μ+1σ μ+2σ μ+3σ

This is called a Normal distribution, and it is described by its average (mean), usually
written μ (the Greek letter mu) and its standard deviation usually written as σ
(sigma). The interest in the standard deviation is that it tells us how far away from
the average we should expect our measurements to be.

68.26 percent	μ +/-1 σ
95.46 percent	μ +/-2 σ
99.73 percent	μ +/-3 σ

From the above figure, we can see that

- 68.3% of our times will be within one standard deviation of the average or mean
- 95.5% will be within two standard deviations of the mean
- 99.7% will be within three standard deviations of the mean

10 What is the formula for calculating standard deviation?

The formula for calculating the standard deviation is:

$$\sigma = \sqrt{\frac{\Sigma (X - \mu)^2}{N}}$$

Σ = sum of $\qquad\qquad$ μ = mean
X = individual value $\qquad$ N = total number of values.

11 What is the linkage between defects per million opportunities (DPMO) and sigma level?

DPMO	Sigma Level
691462	1.0
308538	2.0
66807	3.0
6210	4.0
233	5.0
3.40	6.0

Glossary

Bill Smith Motorola engineer who adopted Deming's statistical process control techniques to understanding process variation. Credited with being the first person to develop the Six Sigma concept.

Central limit theorem The central limit theorem is a rule in statistics that demonstrates that in large enough samples, the distribution of a sample mean approximates a normal curve, amazingly, regardless of the shape of the distribution from which it is sampled. The larger the value of the sample size (n) the better the approximation to the normal.

Common Cause Variation Any value that falls within a process' UCL and LCL. Common cause variation is ever-present and is a result of standard work methods and practices. Reduction of common cause variation is via a structured process such as Six Sigma.

Control Chart A data plot which measures data over time or occurrences. Monitors variance in a process over time and alerts the business to unexpected variance which may cause defects. Control charts have UCL and LCL set.

Defect A product's or service's non-fulfilment of an intended requirement or reasonable expectation for use.

Deming, W Edwards American statistician and management consultant who introduced statistical process control and management techniques to the Japanese in the 1950s. The Deming Prize, Japan's most prestigious quality award is named in his honour.

DPMO DPMO is an acronym for 'Defects Per Million Opportunities'. It is a Six Sigma terminology – 6σ equates to a DPMO of 3.4

DMAIC Acronym for Design, Measure, Analyse, Improve and Control. The Six Sigma improvement process.

Flow Chart A graphical representation of the inputs, activities and outputs of processes.

Frequency distribution Summarises process data and graphically represents it in the form a histogram. It reveals the centring, variation and shape of the data.

Lower Control Limit – LCL A statistical measure defined as being three (3) standard deviations below the mean. Used on a control chart to determine whether the process is stable.

Lower Specification Limit – LSL Minimum level of tolerance the customer is willing to accept.

Mean The arithmetic mean is the average of the set of numbers. It is a measure of central tendency.

Median The central value in a set of numbers: half the numbers lie on either side of this value.

Mode The most frequently occurring value in a set of numbers.

Normal distribution A symmetric bell-shaped frequency distribution. Called 'normal' because it is similar to many real-world distributions. The normal distribution is completely determined by its mean and standard deviation.

Performance matrix Chart and accompanying graph which is used to measure performance against goals and targets. Allows you to measure any type of performance at daily, weekly, and monthly intervals.

Process Capability A description of a process' performance in statistical terms stating the UCL, LCL and mean. Used to determine whether a process can consistently meet customer expectations.

Process Shift and Drift Movement over time in a process' performance, as measured by its frequency distribution, as a result of common cause variation.

Run chart
A data plot which measures data over time or occurrences. UCL and LCL are not calculated.

σ Lower case symbol for sigma. In statistics this is used to signify the standard deviation.

Σ Upper case symbol for sigma. In statistics this is used to signify 'the sum of'.

SIPOC Acronym for Suppliers, Inputs, Processes, Outputs and Customers. Provides an easy to understand framework for work flows and customer needs and requirements.

Six Sigma A quality goal which equates to only 3.4 defects per million opportunities for each product or service transaction.

Special Cause Variation Any value that falls outside a process' UCL or LCL. Any special cause variation must be investigated immediately to determine the cause and any necessary action.

Specification Limits Customers' requirements specified in terms minimum and maximum requirements.

Stable process A process where all variation is common cause.

Standard deviation A measure of variation referred to as sigma (σ). The standard deviation measures the average amount the values deviate from the mean. The greater the values are spread out, the larger the standard deviation and therefore the greater the variation.

Statistical Process Control The application of statistical methods to analyse data, study and monitor process capability and performance.

System Rigging Faking or manipulating data.

Tampering Action taken on a process to 'fix it' when you do not know or understand the causes of variation within a process.

Unstable Process A process where there are many special causes.

Upper Control Limit UCL A statistical measure defined as being three (3) standard deviations above the mean. Used on a control chart to determine whether the process is stable.

Upper Specification Limit USL Maximum level of tolerance the customer is willing to accept.

Variation A change (small or large) in a process or business practice that may alter its expected outcome. The difference, however minute, between so called 'identical' processes or products.

Voice of the customer (VOC) Data representing customer needs, expectations and requirements. These are the things that customers are interested in and care about. VOC entails discussing, quantifying and documenting these on an ongoing basis.

Resources

Index

Further Reading.

Six sigma memory jogger –
Black belt guide –
Design for six sigma.